OUR SATELLITE:
THE MOON

Contents

OUR SATELLITE:
THE MOON

Belitha Press

r.i.p tara x

The Earth and the Moon

The Moon is our nearest neighbour in outer space. It is the **celestial body** closest to us, and it accompanies the Earth in its annual voyage around the Sun. The Moon is Earth's only natural **satellite**.

The terrestrial planets

Mercury, Venus, Earth and Mars are the four terrestrial planets. These are the planets closest to the Sun. They have very few satellites: Mercury and Venus have none; Earth, one; and Mars, two. But the Moon is an unusual satellite. It is much larger than the tiny satellites of Mars, and more like the larger satellites of the **giant planets**.

The formation of the Moon

Scientists do not know exactly how the Moon was formed. At one time it was thought that the Earth once rotated much faster than it does now, and that the Moon was formed from material thrown off the Earth by this fast rotation.

Most scientists now believe that the Moon was formed at the same time as the Earth from the same cloud or nebula of gas and dust that formed the Solar System, or from the remains of the material which first condensed to form the Earth. So, instead of considering the Moon to be the Earth's 'daughter' we should consider the earth and the moon to be 'sisters'.

MOON FACTS

Distance from Earth: 384 000 km
   (30 times greater than Earth's diameter).
Time it takes to orbit Earth: 27.3 days.
Diameter: 3 476 km
   (27% of Earth's diameter).
Surface area: 7% that of Earth.
Volume: 2% that of Earth.
Gravity: 17% of Earth's gravity.

Below: The Moon is exceptionally large in proportion to the size of the Earth. Some of the other satellites in the Solar System are also large but are much smaller in comparison to their own planets.

Below: The Moon is Earth's only natural satellite. It is one of the largest satellites in the Solar System. Only four satellites (Io, Ganymede and Callisto of Jupiter, and Titan of Saturn) are slightly larger than the Moon. The Moon's **diameter** is more than a quarter of Earth's diameter. Only one planet in the Solar System can beat this. Pluto has a satellite called Charon, whose diameter is half that of Pluto. But Pluto is about the same size as our Moon, so Charon is much smaller than our Moon.

Exploration of the Moon

The Moon has been explored more than all the other celestial bodies put together. Exploration of the Moon began two years after the launch of *Sputnik 1* in 1957. This was the first artificial satellite of the Earth and the beginning of the space era.

The first **lunar probes** were launched to pass close to the Moon. This is what the Soviet probe *Luna 3* did. The American Ranger space probes were launched to crash against the Moon's surface.

A soft landing

The later space probes were of two types. Some spacecraft were designed to make a soft landing on the Moon's surface, such as the Soviet *Luna 9* and the American Surveyor probes. Other probes were sent into orbit around the Moon. This opened the way for direct exploration of the Moon.

Manned spacecraft

The United States chose to send manned spacecraft to the Moon. Six **Apollo** spacecraft landed and their astronauts explored the area around the landing site. They collected lunar rock samples and left behind instruments which continued to function for years.

The Soviet Union chose to explore the moon using unmanned stations. Some of these collected lunar rock samples and returned to Earth. Others unloaded the **Lunokhod** exploration vehicles.

Below: The Moon has been explored by soft-landing automatic probes and by Lunokhod exploration vehicles, as well as by astronauts.

MAJOR SPACE PROBES TO SUCCESSFULLY LAND ON THE MOON			
Name	**Date**	**Landing area**	**Mission objective**
Luna 9	1966	Ocean of Storms	photographic exploration
Luna 13	1969	Ocean of Storms	ground study
Apollo 11	1969	Sea of Tranquillity	1st manned mission
Apollo 12	1969	Ocean of Storms	2nd manned mission
Luna 17	1970	Sea of Showers	Lunokhod 1 vehicle
Apollo 14	1971	Region of Fra Mauro	3rd manned mission
Apollo 15	1971	Apennine Mountains	4th manned mission
Luna 20	1972	Sea of Fertility	collecting samples
Apollo 16	1972	Region of Descartes	5th manned mission
Apollo 17	1972	Taurus-Littrow Region	6th manned mission
Luna 21	1973	Region of Lemmonier	Lunokhod 2 vehicle
Luna 24	1976	Sea of Crises	collecting samples

Below: The Moon is the only celestial body to have been directly explored by human beings. Only 12 astronauts have walked on the Moon's surface. From 1969 to 1972 six Apollo missions reached the Moon, each carrying three astronauts. One person remained in orbit around the Moon while the other two landed to gather rock samples and carry out a series of experiments. On two of the Apollo missions, the astronauts drove a Lunar Roving Vehicle, pictured below. There have been no landings on the Moon by astronauts since 1972.

The phases of the Moon

The Moon, like the other planets and satellites in our Solar System, does not give off any light of its own. The Moon shines in the night sky because it reflects sunlight. Half the Moon's surface, the hemisphere that faces the Sun, is lit up, while the other half is dark.

The Moon travels around the Earth from west to east. The Moon's shape seems to change in a pattern that repeats every month. The different shapes of the Moon are called **lunar phases**.

The new Moon

The new Moon occurs when the lighted surface of the Moon faces away from us so we cannot see it. This happens when the Moon, on its orbit around the Earth, passes between the Earth and the Sun.

The Moon is in its first quarter when it has travelled a quarter of its orbit around the Earth, a week after the new Moon. Another week later, we see the Moon completely lit up because it is now opposite the Sun. This is the full Moon. In the last quarter, another week later, we see only half of the Moon's disc.

The Moon's cycle

When 29 1/2 days have passed since the last new Moon, the Moon again lines up with the Sun, ready to begin another cycle of its phases. This cycle is repeated just over 12 times during one year.

Below: The Moon takes about a week to change phase and advance a quarter of its orbit around the Earth.

Below: The crescent of the Moon is seen at dusk near the western horizon just after sunset. The lit-up face of the Moon is the part which faces the Sun.

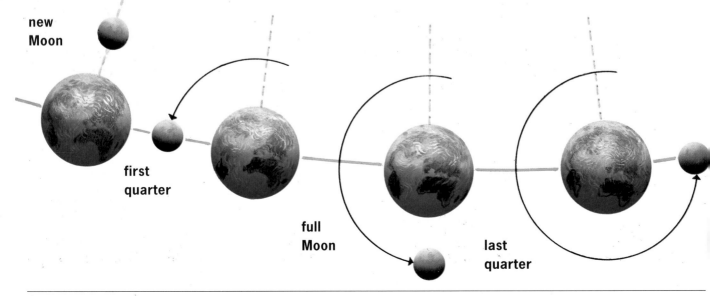

new
Moon

first
quarter

full
Moon

last
quarter

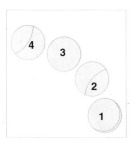

Below: A few days after the new Moon [1], the Moon appears in the sky in the shape of a thin wedge of melon. The Moon is now in its first quarter. It is seen in the west at dusk, setting on the horizon shortly after the Sun sets. When the Moon is in its first quarter [2], we see half of the hemisphere facing us lit up by the Sun. During the full Moon [3], the Moon rises above the horizon just as the Sun sets. During the last quarter [4], the Moon does not rise until late at night.

Eclipses

The Earth and Moon project long shadows in space, in the opposite direction from the Sun. These shadows are shaped like cones. When the Earth passes through the Moon's **shadow cone** an eclipse of the Sun, or **solar eclipse**, occurs on Earth. This is because the Moon passes in front of the Sun and hides it from our view.

Lunar eclipses

In the same way, when the Moon passes through the Earth's shadow cone, the Moon is no longer lit up by the Sun, and on Earth we see an eclipse of the Moon, or **lunar eclipse**. Every year there are between two and seven eclipses of the Sun and the Moon.

Looking at eclipses

There are about the same number of solar eclipses as lunar eclipses, but we can see the lunar eclipses from much larger areas of the Earth. By contrast, solar eclipses can only be seen from a very small area, under the Moon's shadow cone.

During an eclipse of the Moon, when the Moon enters Earth's shadow cone, we can see how the Earth's shadow slowly covers the disc of the full Moon. During a partial lunar eclipse, only part of the Moon is in Earth's shadow. A total lunar eclipse can last over an hour.

Below: The Moon's orbit is tilted slightly to the plane of the Earth's orbit. If the two orbits were in the same plane, there would be a lunar eclipse every full Moon and a solar eclipse every new Moon. Most months the Moon passes above or below the Earth's shadow cone.

LUNAR ECLIPSES FROM 1995 TO 2000	
Date	**Type**
15 Apr 1995	partial
3-4 Apr 1996	total
27 Sept 1996	total
24 Mar 1997	partial
16 Sept 1997	total
28 July 1999	partial
21 Jan 2000	total
16 July 2000	total

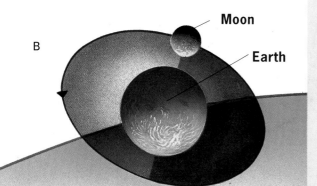

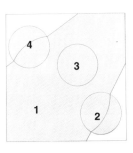

Below: When a lunar eclipse occurs, the Moon enters into the Earth's shadow cone [1]. The Sun's light, which usually lights up the Moon, is blocked by Earth. The Earth's shadow starts to cover the eastern part of the Moon's disc [2]. When the Moon has completely entered the shadow cone, the total eclipse occurs [3]. At the end of the eclipse, the eastern edge of the Moon starts to come out of the shadow cone and is lit up once again [4].

Looking at an eclipse of the Moon

Lunar eclipses are quite frequent and are easy to look at. They can usually be seen from a particular place on Earth every year as long as clouds do not hide them from view. An eclipse of the Moon is a beautiful sight which can be seen by the naked eye (without using a telescope or binoculars). You can use binoculars, if you have a pair or can borrow some.

Earth's shadow

When the Moon comes between the Sun and the Earth, the eastern edge of the lunar disc darkens. The eastern side of the Moon's disc is dark because it is that side which first moves into shadow.

When the Moon enters the Earth's shadow in the east, the Earth comes between the Sun and Moon and blocks out the sunlight reaching the Moon.

A perfect circle

As the Earth's shadow sweeps over the Moon, look at its shape. You will see that it forms a circle. This shows that the Earth is **spherical,** because the sphere is the only shape that makes a shadow which is always circular no matter which direction light shines from.

Moving very slowly

If you watch a lunar eclipse, try to imagine the Earth's shadow cone in space, and the Moon moving slowly into it. Although the Moon appears to be moving very slowly, it is actually travelling through space at more than 3 000 kilometres per hour!

Below: In a solar eclipse, the Moon comes between the Sun and the Earth. The Moon's shadow cone only covers a small part of the Earth's surface. From this area a total eclipse of the Sun can be observed. In an eclipse of the Moon, the Earth comes between the Sun and the Moon, and the Moon enters the Earth's shadow.

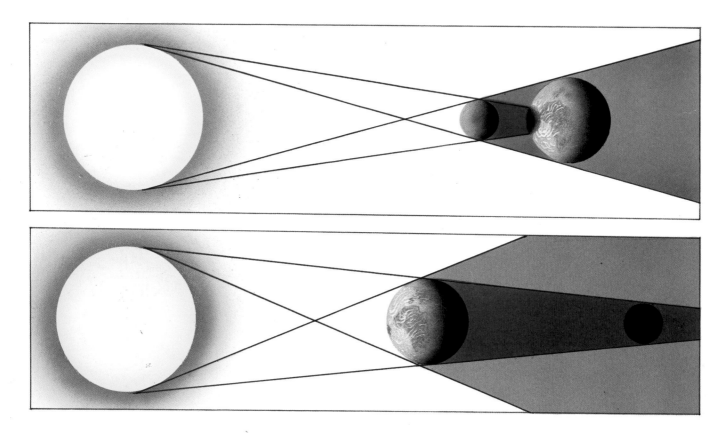

Below: In a lunar eclipse, the part of the Moon covered by the Earth's shadow [1] is not completely invisible. It is illuminated by a faint dark-red light. This reddish light fills the shadow projected by the Earth [2] into outer space. This colour is produced by sunlight passing through the Earth's atmosphere. The blue part of sunlight is scattered throughout the atmosphere, giving the sky its blue colour. Most of the red light gets through and reaches the Moon, giving it a reddish tinge.

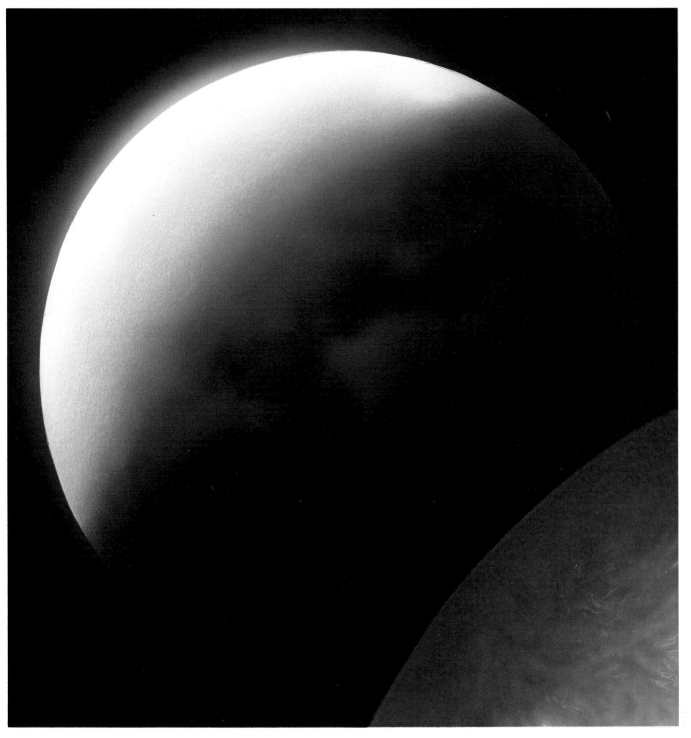

The tides

Everyone that has ever been to the sea-side knows about tides. The level of the tide rises and falls twice every day. The rhythm of the tides affects the activities of people who work on or near the sea.

Changing tides

For hundreds of years, people have known that the tides come about 50 minutes later every day, just as the Moon rises 50 minutes later every day. The force of the Moon's **gravitational pull** is part of what causes the tides.

The Moon's influence

The influence of the Moon's gravitational pull is greater than the Sun's influence, because the Moon is much closer to the Earth. The size of the force that causes the tides – the tidal force – depends upon the difference between two points on the Earth. So a nearby object such as the Moon produces a greater tidal force than the distant Sun.

Water bulges

Imagine the Earth is covered by a layer of water. The Moon will attract the water closest to it with a greater force than it exerts at the centre of the Earth. It pulls at the Earth's centre with greater force than it exerts on the water on the far side. This makes the water bulge out at two places in line with the Moon.

High and low tides

The bulges occur at two places on the Earth at any one time. At any one point on the Earth we will see two rises in the water level (**high tides**) and two times when the water falls (**low tides**) for each rotation of the Earth.

Left: The Sun has much less influence on the tides than the Moon. But when the Sun is in line with the Moon, it reinforces the action of the Moon. This produces the highest high tides which we call **spring tides**. These occur during the full Moon and new Moon. When the Sun is not in line with the Moon in the first quarter and last quarter, high tides are lower and are called **neap tides**.

Below: The succession of low tides (left) and high tides (right) occurs twice a day.

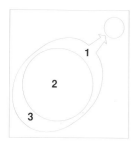

Below: The Moon's gravitational attraction is stronger on the part of Earth facing the Moon [1] than it is at the centre of the Earth [2]. In turn, this force is more intense at the centre of the Earth than it is at the part of the Earth facing away from the Moon. This causes two bulges of water which form a straight line with the Moon. We see these bulges as the regular rising and falling of the tides.

The Moon's evolution

Even though the Moon is very close to the Earth, its surface looks completely different from the Earth's surface. The main reason for this is that the Moon is small and has a relatively weak force of gravitational attraction so it cannot retain an atmosphere like the atmosphere surrounding Earth.

Erosion

On Earth, there are no longer any traces of the ancient **craters** which were produced by the numerous **meteorites** that fell to Earth shortly after the planets of the Solar System formed. The craters have gradually been worn away by wind, rain, rivers and sea. This is erosion. Today, the Earth's atmosphere protects it from the small meteorites which fall towards it, burning up before they reach the Earth's surface.

Moon craters

On the Moon, once craters are produced they remain unchanged unless another meteorite later falls in the same place. Many of the **depressions** produced by the impact of large meteorites when the Moon was still young became flooded by lava which flowed out of the many volcanoes that existed at that time.

The oldest regions

The number of craters found in different areas of the Moon tell us how old the surface is in that area. The longer an area has been bombarded by meteorites, the more craters there are on its surface. So the flat surfaces of the Moon, the **lunar maria,** are the youngest regions and have few craters. The oldest regions are completely covered by craters, many of which appear one on top of another.

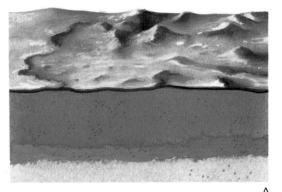

A

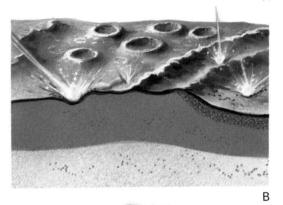

B

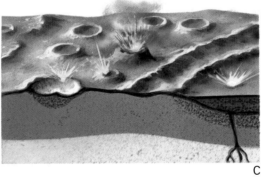

C

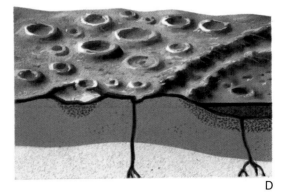

D

Left:
A This is how the surface of the Moon appeared 4 000 million years ago when the Moon had just been formed.

B Later the Moon's surface was changed by the constant showers of falling meteorites.

C About 3 000 million years ago, intense volcanic activity occurred. The lava thrown out by volcanoes flooded the ancient craters and formed the lunar maria.

D When the volcanic activity stopped, the appearance of the lunar surface was changed again by the impact of falling meteorites, which created new craters.

Structure of the Moon

The Moon is made of a material which is lighter than that of Earth: its **density** is only 0.6 times that of Earth. This makes scientists think that the core or central part of the Moon which is made of heavy elements such as iron, is relatively small. It is about 1 000 km in diameter. There is a rocky **mantle** around the core.

Lunar quakes
The base of the mantle is where the small lunar quakes start. These quakes occur regularly on the Moon. They have been discovered by **seismographs** left behind on the Moon's surface by Apollo astronauts. The information collected by these instruments shows that the Moon's interior is made up of molten material like the interior of the Earth.

The Moon's crust
The top layer of the Moon is called the crust. It is about 60 km thick and even thicker on the far side. The upper layer of the crust is made up of the remains of rock fragments of all sizes called **regolith**. This pulverized rock is the result of the bombardment of the Moon's surface by meteorites that has taken place since its formation. The regolith layer is normally between 5 and 10 metres deep but is a bit thinner in the area of the lunar maria.

The pulverized rock layer that covers the entire surface of the Moon is what gives it its dusty appearance. Scientists were afraid that this dust layer would swallow up any object placed on the Moon's surface. This idea was proved wrong when the first space probe landed. The probe did not sink. The Moon's surface was able to support its weight.

Lunar rocks
The Apollo space missions and Luna automatic space probes brought back many samples of lunar rocks to Earth. These have been studied in detail. Scientists have found that they are basalt rocks more or less similar to some types of volcanic lava found on Earth.

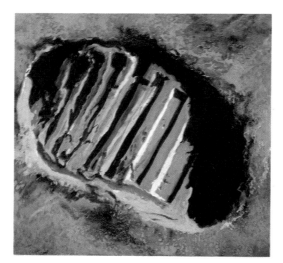

A

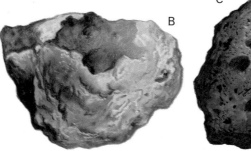

B

C

Left: The footprints of the astronauts sink into the dust to a depth of several centimetres. Since there is no erosion on the Moon, these footprints will always remain visible on the Moon's surface.

Lower left: About 400 kg of lunar rocks have been analysed, such as those shown here. They were brought back by the Apollo and Luna missions. They are all volcanic rocks, such as basalt that we find here on Earth.

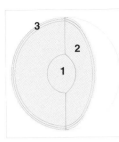

Below: The Moon has a relatively small core [1], in which the heaviest materials, such as iron, are concentrated. Around the core, there is a molten rocky mantle [2]. The surface crust [3] is thicker on the far side of the Moon than on the side nearest Earth. This crust is covered by a regolith layer of dust and rock fragments of all sizes produced by the constant bombardment of the Moon by meteorites.

The Moon's visible side

The tidal force that the Moon produces on Earth tends to slow down the Earth's rotation and make the day longer. In the same way, the Earth exerts a tidal force on the Moon, and this is much stronger.

A lunar day
The Moon takes the same time to rotate once on its axis as it does to orbit the Earth, so a day on the Moon takes one Earth month. This is why the same half of the Moon is always turned to Earth. This is not a coincidence. The force that causes tides in the Earth's oceans is also slowing the Earth's rotation very gradually. Over millions of years, the Earth has exerted a similar force on the Moon, slowing its rotation to its current speed.

Lunar seas
So from Earth we always see the same side of the Moon. When we look at it we can see some large dark spots. These dark regions are called lunar seas or maria because scientists first thought they were areas covered with water. We now know that they are actually covered with solidified volcanic lava.

The terminator
The visible side of the Moon has a surface covered with craters except in the areas of the maria, which are much smoother. The craters are most easily seen in an area called the **terminator**. This is the thin area separating the light and shadowed sides.

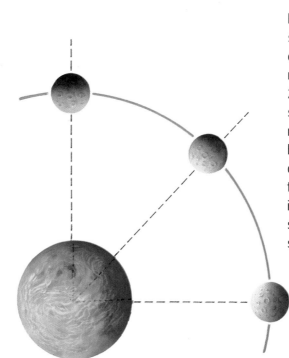

Left: The Moon spins on its axis, completing a rotation once every 27 days. At the same time it revolves around Earth completing one orbit in exactly the same time. This is why it always shows the same side to the Earth.

Right: The Moon has two features on its surface which are most outstanding: large depressions filled with dark, solidified lava called seas; and large craters produced by the impact of falling meteorites on the Moon's surface.

Below: You can use a pair of binoculars to see the visible side of the Moon more closely. The large dark patches look like vast plains. These are the lunar seas. The large craters can also be seen easily and, if you use a map, you can find out which one is which and what each crater is called. Full Moon is not the best time to do this. At this time, the Sun's light strikes the Moon's surface head-on, and makes it difficult to see the **relief** of the moonscape. It is much better to observe the Moon in the first or last quarter phases.

Lunar maria

The lunar maria or seas cover a large part of the visible face of the Moon. These are regions that look darker than the rest of the Moon's surface. The lunar maria are relatively smooth, having few craters. So we know that the surface of the lunar seas is younger than the rest of the Moon's surface.

Volcanic activity

The lunar maria were once large depressions in the surface of the Moon made by the impact of large meteorites shortly after the Moon was formed. The edges of these depressions form circular mountain ranges which surround the craters. About 3 000 million years ago, the Moon experienced a lot of volcanic activity. Lava flowed out of the volcanoes and filled the depressions, forming the lunar maria we see today.

Sea of Crises

Some of these seas are in the shape of a circle and are separate from the rest. One of these is the Sea of Crises, which is in the northern hemisphere of the moon near the western edge. This is the crater we see during the first quarter, a few days after the new Moon. Just under this sea we can see another dark patch which is the Sea of Fertility.

Three more seas

When the Moon is in the first quarter, another longish dark patch can be seen which is three different seas connected together: from north to south, these are the Sea of Serenity, the Sea of Tranquillity (where a human set foot on the Moon for the first time) and the Sea of Nectar.

In the eastern hemisphere, which is visible when the Moon is full or in the last quarter, there is a group of large seas connected together. The largest is the Sea of Rains, which is surrounded by high mountain ranges. Some of the smaller maria are in the south. These include the Sea of Moisture and the Sea of Clouds.

THE LUNAR MARIA
Sea of Fertility (Mare Foecundatis)
Sea of Serenity (Mare Serenitatis)
Sea of Tranquillity (Mare Tranquillitatis)
Sea of Crises (Mare Crisium)
Sea of Showers (Mare Imbrium)
Sea of Clouds (Mare Nubrium)
Sea of Moisture (Mare Humorium)
Sea of Vapours (Mare Vaporum)
Sea of Cold (Mare Frigoris)
Sea of Nectar (Mare Nectaris)
Ocean of Storms (Oceanus Procellarum)

Below: The lunar seas are large depressions filled with solidified lava. The depressions were formed when the Moon was young when large meteorites crashed onto its surface. Later, lava flowing from many volcanoes flooded the depressions, making a flat surface which later became scattered with craters.

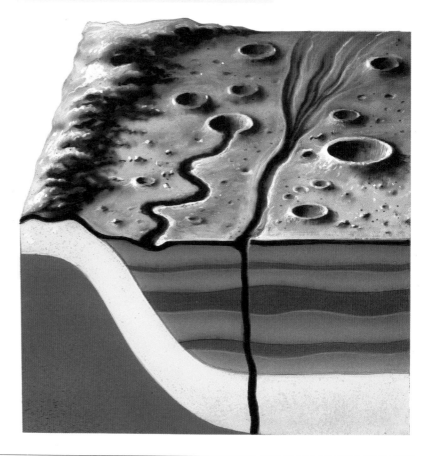

Below: The Bay of Rainbows is located in the northern half of the visible side of the Moon. It is an old crater formed by the impact of a large meteorite about 4 000 million years ago. The depression later became partially filled by the volcanic lava that also produced the Sea of Rains. This area shows us the difference between a sea in the south which is flat and has only a few craters, and a mountainous region in the north which has sharp, craggy contours and lots of craters.

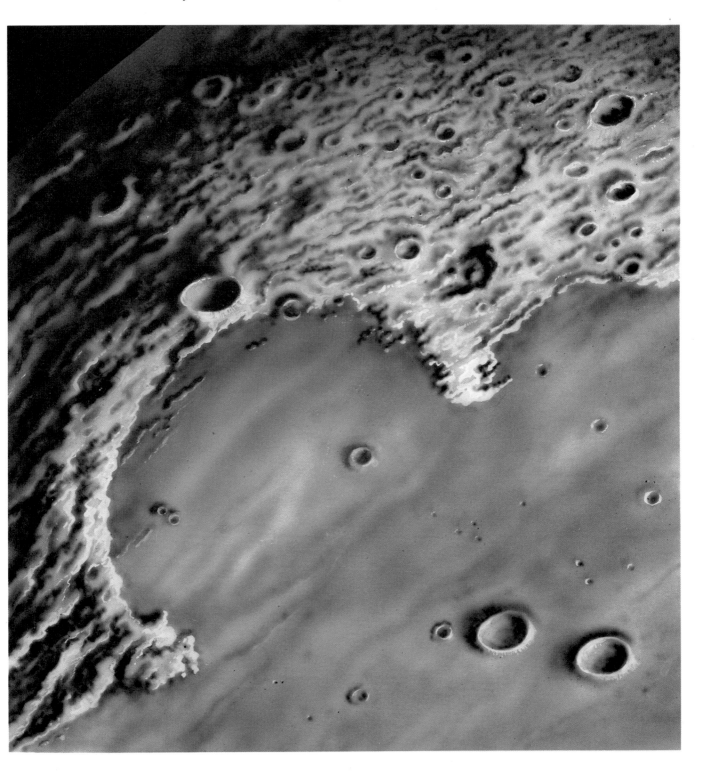

Lunar craters

Most of the Moon's surface is covered with craters. Craters are shaped like circles, have sunken bottoms and edges which are slightly higher than the rest of the Moon's surface. The walls of the edges are not steep but rise gently from the bottom of the crater.

Some craters have one or more peaks in their centres, and others have a smooth bottom. Often traces of debris from the impact and smaller secondary craters surround large craters.

Different sizes

There are craters of all sizes on the Moon. The smallest are microscopic, while the largest are more easily visible and can be as wide as 100 or 200 km.

Tycho

Tycho is a very large crater and has a diameter of 80 km. It forms part of a mountainous zone in the south part of the moon below the Sea of Clouds.

When Tycho is brightly illuminated by the Sun, during the full Moon, brilliant lines appear in the ground and shine out of the crater for a great distance. These lines are formed by material that was thrown out when the crater was formed.

The origin of craters

Most scientists now believe that the great majority of craters, like Tycho, were formed by the impact of meteorites crashing onto the Moon's surface.

Some craters were formed by volcanic activity. We recognize these by their smooth lava-covered bottoms which have no peaks in the centre. One volcanic crater is Herodotus which is beside the impact crater known as Aristarchus.

THE LARGEST LUNAR CRATERS

Alphonsus	Herodotus
Aristarchus	Hipparchus
Aristotle	Kepler
Archimedes	Plato
Clavius	Theophilus
Copernicus	Tycho
Eudoxus	

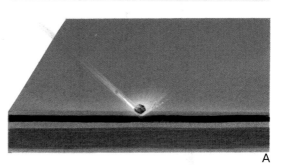

Left:

A Meteorites crash into the Moon's surface. Unlike the Earth, the Moon has no atmosphere to protect it.

B The impact breaks up the meteorite and throws out material from the surface.

C As the material is sent flying in all directions, a round crater forms with a hollow depression in the centre.

D The edge of the crater forms a mountainous ring that rises above the surrounding surface.

bored.

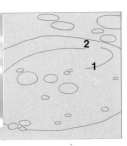

Below: Copernicus, one of the Moon's largest craters, is over 90 km wide. Found near the Ocean of Storms, Copernicus is a good example of craters created by the impact of falling meteorites. Its bottom is very irregular and has many mountain peaks [1]. This crater has sharply sloping walls [2] which rise as high as 5 km above the bottom of the crater.

The far side of the Moon

The Moon takes the same time to spin on its axis as to orbit Earth. For this reason, one side of the Moon remains out of view from the Earth at all times. In fact, because we can look at the Moon from different places on Earth and since the Moon also wobbles slightly as it moves around the Earth, we can see a bit more than half of the Moon's surface. Over 40% of its surface still remains hidden when we look at the Moon from Earth.

The far side
In 1959, at the beginning of the space era, the Soviet space probe *Luna 3* managed to travel behind the Moon. The lunar probe sent back the first images of the **far side** of the Moon. These first photographs revealed that the far side of the Moon is similar to the side we can see, but there are some differences.

Covered with craters
The far side of the Moon is almost totally covered with craters, although they are not as large as those on the visible side of the Moon.

   The largest seas are close to the edge of the visible side, and these can be seen, in part, from the Earth. One of the most important of these is the Eastern Sea, a large depression which is about 900 km in diameter.

The same side
The differences between the two sides of the Moon tell us that the Moon has always shown the same side to Earth. The differences also tell us how the inside of the Moon is made up. Its crust, which is about 60 km thick on the visible side, is much thicker on the hidden side.

Above: The Tsiolkovsky crater is one of the darkest on the Moon.

Below: The Oriental Sea is a large depression, 900 km in diameter, which is filled with dark lava and surrounded by rings of mountains.

Below: The far side of the Moon was a mystery until 1959 when the *Luna 3* space probe photographed it for the first time. The hidden side is almost completely covered with craters, but has very few maria. One of the most important of these seas is the Eastern Sea, whose mountains cover a large part of the Moon's surface. The Moscow Sea is one of the few maria which is completely within the far side. It is small, dark and circular, and it was first discovered by the *Luna 3* images.

Activity: Earth and Moon models

We know that the Moon is more or less a quarter the size of the Earth and that it is about 30 times the Earth's diameter away from us. You don't need a powerful telescope or a trip in a spaceship to look at the Earth-Moon system. Instead you can make a model of the Earth and Moon yourself and look at the phases of the Moon and the eclipses in your own back garden or in the park.

You will need:

1 ball about 1cm in diameter
1 ball about 4cm in diameter
a hammer and 2 long nails
a wooden stick 120cm long

If you can't find balls the right size you can make your own from plasticine – these will be just as good.

Making your Earth-Moon model

1 Take the hammer and hammer the two nails into the stick, one at each end. The nails need to be long enough to pierce the wood so that the points stick out about 1cm. Ask an adult for help if you need it.
2 Take the large ball and stick it onto the end of one of the nails on the stick.
3 Put the other ball on the nail at the other end of the stick.

You should now have a model of the Earth-Moon system which you can use to look at the phases of the Moon and the eclipses.

What to do

1 Choose a sunny day when you can see the Moon in the sky (in the morning if the Moon is in its last quarter, or in the afternoon if it is in its first quarter).
2 Take your Earth-Moon system model and find a place that is bright and sunny.
3 Now put the large ball which is Earth close to your eye and point the stick towards where you can see the real Moon in the sky.

You will see that the Moon-ball and the real Moon seem the same size. They are lit up by the Sun in the same way. You are now looking at a phase of the Moon.

4 Now stand with the Sun to one side and hold the stick in both hands with the Earth-ball pointing towards the Sun and the Moon-ball towards the ground.

4cm ball for the Earth

1cm ball for the Moon

120cm stick

Right: If you point the stick towards the Moon, you will see the Moon-ball lit up by the Sun in the same phase as the real Moon.

Below: If you line up the Sun, the Earth-ball and the Moon-ball, the Moon-ball is left dark. This is an eclipse of the Moon.

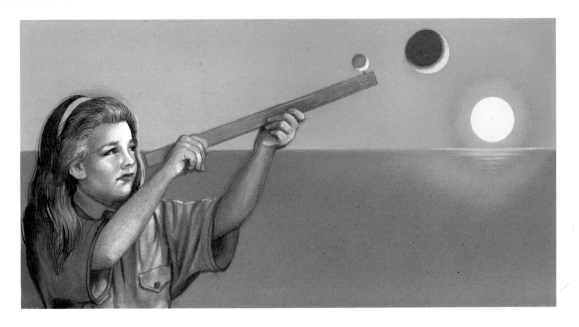

5 Line up the stick with the Sun (you can use the stick's shadow on the ground to help you).
6 Now line up the Sun, the Earth-ball and the Moon-ball.

You will see how the Earth blocks the Moon from the Sun. This is an eclipse of the Moon.

Warning: NEVER look directly at the Sun – it can damage your eyes and cause blindness.

Glossary

Apollo American lunar exploration programme that used manned spaceships.

celestial body Star, planet or other natural object in space.

crater A circular depression that has an edge which is higher than the surrounding lunar surface. Most lunar craters were produced by the impact of meteorites. These are also called lunar rings.

density A measure of how tightly packed is the matter in a substance.

depressions A dent or hollow in a surface.

diameter The length of a straight line which runs from one side of a circle to another, passing through the centre.

giant planets The giant planets are the largest planets in the universe and are made up mainly of gases. They are surrounded by families of satellites.

gravitational pull or **force** The mutual attraction of the masses of two objects, especially celestial bodies.

high tide This is when the tide reaches its highest point.

low tide This is when the tide is at its lowest point.

lunar eclipse An eclipse of the Moon or lunar eclipse occurs when the Earth comes between the Moon and the Sun.

lunar phases Changes in the apparent shape of the Moon as it orbits Earth during the lunar cycle.

lunar probes Spacecraft which were developed to explore the surface of the Moon.

lunar maria or **seas** Dark plains on the surface of the Moon which were formed when volcanic lava filled in ancient lunar depressions.

Lunokhod An automatic unmanned Moon exploration vehicle. Two Lunokhods were unloaded by Soviet space probes and landed on the Moon's surface in 1970 and 1973.

meteorite The remains of a meteor that has not completely burned up on its journey through the Earth's atmosphere, and has landed on the Earth's surface.

neap tide A very low tide that occurs twice a month when the Moon is in its first or third quarter.

regolith Fragments of rock of all sizes which make up the dusty layer on the surface of the Moon.

relief The raised parts of a surface. The mountains of the Moon are in relief.

satellite Any object which orbits one of the planets.

seismograph An instrument to measure movement or tremors on the surface of a planet or satellite.

shadow cone An area in space which sunlight does not reach because it is blocked out by a planet or satellite.

solar eclipse This occurs when the Moon comes between Earth and the Sun and cuts off sunlight.

spherical Round like a ball.

spring tide A very high tide which occurs when the Sun and Moon line up during the phases of the full Moon and new Moon.

terminator The area between the part of the Moon which is lit up and the dark part. This is where we can see the greatest differences in the shape of the Moon's surface because the shadows are larger.

tide The rise and fall of the level of the sea caused mainly by the Moon's gravitational attraction, and partly by the Sun's gravitational attraction.

© Parramón Ediciones, SA 1992

First published in the United Kingdom in 1994 by

 Belitha Press Limited
31 Newington Green
London N16 9PU

English translation © 1994 by Barron's Educational Series Inc.

Cataloguing in print data available from the British Library.

ISBN 1 85561 368 9

Consultant: Jack Challoner

Series designer: Hayley Cove
Series editor: Maria O'Neill

Index

Words in **bold** appear in the glossary on pages 30 and 31.